Girl's
Sticker
Activity Book

The Alligator logo is a registered trade mark of Alligator Products Limited.
© 2017 Alligator Products Limited.
Published by Alligator Products Limited,
2nd Floor, 314 Regents Park Road,
London N3 2JX
Retain this address for future use.
Printed in China.0533

Yummy Cakes

Now you can make these cakes even tastier! Just find all the yummy stickers to decorate the cakes. Tuck in!

It's Bedtime!

Somebody is feeling sleepy! But before you go to sleep you need to decorate the bed with lots of cute stickers!

Looking Like a Princess

Help this princess get ready for the ball. Colour the dress in any colour you like, then look for the bow, shoe and star stickers to finish the picture.

Sticker

Sticker

Sticker

Sticker

Sticker

Sticker

Sticker

Sticker

Sticker

Sticker

Sticker

Sticker

Sticker

Sticker

Fairy Magic!

Sticker

Sticker

Sticker

There's some magic in the air today! Place the crown, star and skirt stickers onto the fairy, then get creative and colour in the flowers.

House Repairs

This house needs brightening up! First of all, go and find the colour stickers and stick them in their place. Each colour has its own number. Find the number on the picture and colour in the area.

Blue Sticker	Red Sticker	Yellow Sticker	Green Sticker	Brown Sticker
Number 1	Number 2	Number 3	Number 4	Number 5

Cat's Playtime

Cats like nothing better than to play!
On the sticker pages find the 3 cats and the wool. Then you can
find out which cat leads to the ball of wool.

Sticker

Sticker

Sticker

Sticker

Clock Face

Sticker

Sticker

Sticker

Sticker

Sticker

Sticker

Sticker

Sticker

Sticker

Sticker

Sticker

Sticker

Sticker

It's time (ha ha!) to find all the stickers to complete this picture. You'll need the numbers, the clock's hands and the cheeky mouse!

Page 2
Stickers

Page 3
Stickers

Page 4 Stickers

Page 5
Stickers

6 11 3 7

Page 6 Stickers

Page 7
Stickers

9

10 8

4

1

5 12

2

Page 8 Stickers

Page 9
Stickers

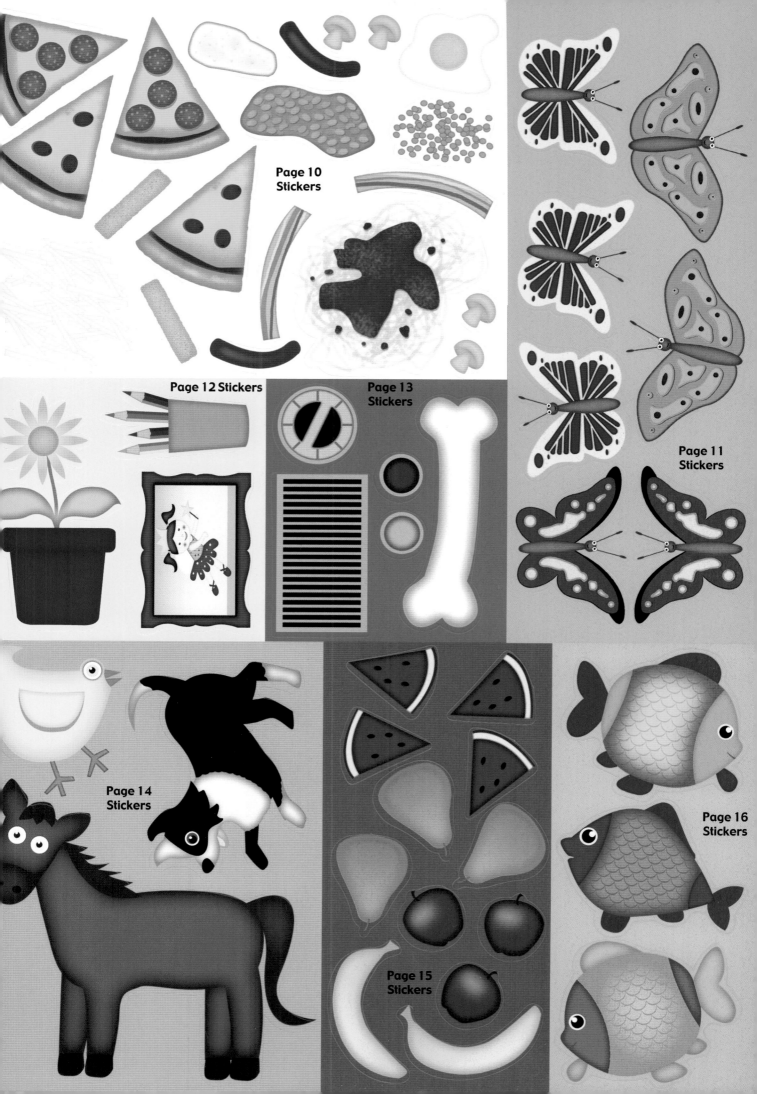

Page 10
Stickers

Page 12 Stickers

Page 13
Stickers

Page 11
Stickers

Page 14
Stickers

Page 15
Stickers

Page 16
Stickers

Animal Match

First of all match up the baby animal stickers with their mummy. Then see if you can write the animal's name in the box provided.

Sticker

Sticker

Sticker

Dinnertime!

What do you fancy to eat?
Have a look at all the delicious food stickers and make up
your favourite plates of yummy food!

Butterfly Fun

Sticker

Sticker

Sticker

Sticker

Sticker

Sticker

Sticker

Colour in the 3 big
butterflies any colour you like.
Then find the 7 butterfly stickers and
see if you can stick the right butterflies
in the correct shaped spaces.

11

Picture This!

What scene would you love to see from this window? You can really use your imagination on this one. Also, don't forget to find the stickers for the window ledge.

Anything on the T.V?

Sticker

Sticker Sticker

Sticker

Sticker

What's your favourite programme on television? Maybe you would like to draw a character from the show on the screen above? Also, make sure you complete the picture with the missing T.V parts and the dog's bone.

Down on the Farm

Take a visit to the farm. First, go and find the different animal stickers, then draw a line to connect the correct animal to its footprint shape.

Sticker

Sticker

Sticker

14

Fruit Adding

This looks like healthy fun!
Find the tasty fruit stickers, then stick them in place.
See if you can count up how many fruits are in each box.
Write your answer in the box provided.

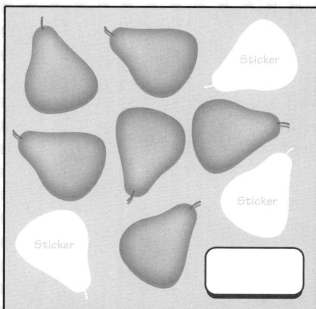

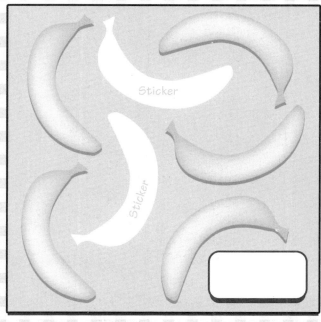

Underwater fishy friends

Sticker

Sticker

Sticker

Wow! Look at all the different fish in the ocean. You can colour in the big fish in the middle, any colour you like. Then find the right fish stickers and stick them in place.

16